The
ANIMALS
of
FARTHING
WOOD ™

ANNUAL 1996

G000153835

£4.99
UK only

Contents

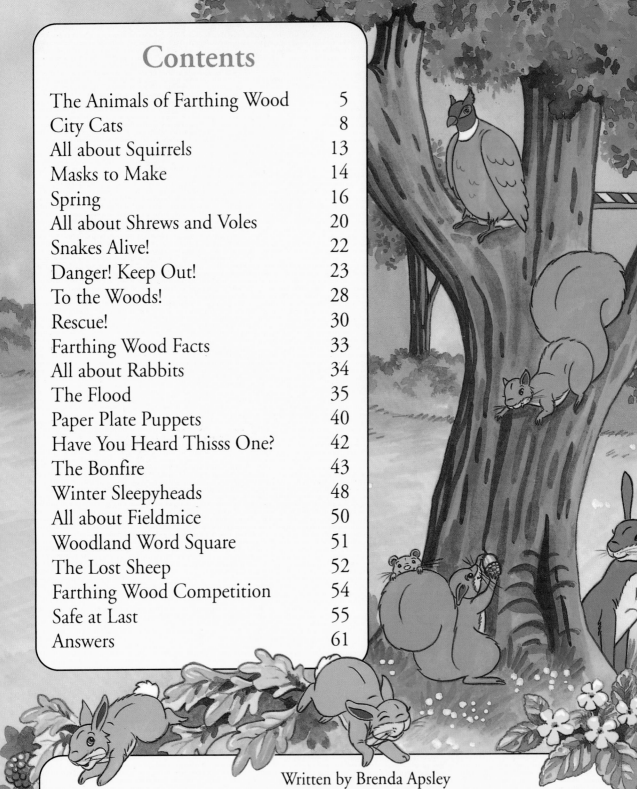

Written by Brenda Apsley
Based on the novels by Colin Dann
Illustrated by Jane Swift

Published in Great Britain in 1995 by World International, an imprint of
Egmont Publishing, Egmont House, PO Box 111, Great Ducie Street, Manchester M60 3BL.
Printed in Italy.   ISBN 0 7498 2315 1

The Animals of Farthing Wood

For the animals who lived in Farthing Wood trouble started when the humans arrived. Before the humans came to Farthing Heath and built their new roads, streets and houses the wood was a good place to live. The trees and plants provided shelter, food and water for all the animals.

Now the humans had come closer still, and started working on the edge of the wood, their whirring chainsaws cutting down old trees and big, noisy machines digging and clearing the ground. There were more and more humans around, and less and less space for the animals.

Soon big trucks arrived. They came every day and poured heaps of stones and rubble into the Farthing Wood pond. There was less and less water for the animals to drink. And without water they would all die.

Every animal in Farthing Wood was in danger.

A meeting of all the animals was called. They had to decide what to do. They agreed that they could not stay in Farthing Wood much longer without safe places to live and clean water to drink.

"The humans are everywhere," said Mrs Rabbit. "I saw one of them peering down our burrow this morning. Soon there will be no space for us."

"But where can we go?" asked a Shrew.

No one had an answer for him – not even wise old Badger.

Just then Toad arrived. Some cruel humans had caught him and taken him home in a jam jar. Though he had managed to escape, it had taken him many weeks to travel back to Farthing Wood. Toad looked around in amazement. "Where has my pond gone?" he asked.

Fox told him how the humans had been filling it in. "I think you've had a wasted journey, Toad," he said.

"There's no home for you here. There's no home here for any of us now."

"Then we'll have to make new homes somewhere else, won't we, mateys?" said Toad.

"But where?" asked Weasel.

"I travelled through a big nature reserve called White Deer Park. It was peaceful there. Lots of trees and open

spaces. We could all live safely there. And there's a big, big pond for me."

"Can you take usss to it?" hissed Adder.

"Course I can!" said Toad. "I'll be your guide."

"Fox, will you be our leader?" asked Badger.

Fox nodded as his keen ears picked up the sounds of machines moving closer and closer.

"We'll all meet at the Great Beech tree and set off tonight."

Later, as a full moon lit up the black sky, the animals gathered. "We must agree to help each other on the journey, and not harm each other," said Badger. "Even though some of us are natural enemies."

The animals all nodded in agreement and held up a paw, wing or claw. They swore the Oath of Mutual Protection. "We promise not to frighten, bully or eat each other on the long journey ahead," they said.

And as the moon slipped behind a cloud the animals of Farthing Wood set off on their great adventure.

7

City Cats

The journey that led the animals from Farthing Wood was a hard one. They rested by day wherever they could find safety and shelter, and travelled by night, when they would not be seen. But the spring nights were sometimes still windy and chilly, and food was not easy to find. After just a few days of travelling some of the animals were looking weak and tired, and ready to give up.

The animals had just started out on another night's long trek when they reached the top of a hill. An amazing sight stretched out in front of them. Hundreds and hundreds of orange dots of light lit up the blackness. Most of the animals had never seen anything like it before.

But Badger had. He knew what it was. "It's the city," he told the others. "A noisy, dangerous place where the humans live. It's no place for us. Come on, we'll go round this way."

Toad knew all about the city, too. He had been there before. He spoke to Badger and Fox quietly, so that the others could not hear. "I knows that there city is dangerous for the likes of us, but there IS food there." He pointed to the small animals. "And this lot need some food bad. Them humans are very wasteful. They throw lots away. Let's go and find some."

Fox looked at the small animals standing around looking sad and miserable. "I think Toad's right, Badger," he said. "Some of the animals won't be willing or able to go on if they don't eat soon. Perhaps we should go into the city to try and find some food."

"Aye," said Toad, touching his nose and winking. "And I think I knows just the place to find it."

Badger looked at the little Fieldmice lying slumped in the grass. "All right. But we must all stick together, and we must be careful, very careful."

Fox told the other animals where they were going. They were all tired, but agreed to go to the city in the hope of finding food. "Come on, then," said Fox. "We must get there and back while it is still dark and the humans are asleep."

The animals soon reached the outskirts of the city. They were about to cross a road when a huge lorry with bright lights appeared and zoomed past them. Badger had to pull one of the Rabbits to safety. As they crossed to the other side of the road a police car whizzed by in front of them, the light on its roof flashing. The loud *nee-naw* sound of the siren made Adder slither under some bricks in fright. "I don't like thisss," she hissed.

"Neither do I," said Badger. "Go into that dark alleyway over there, everyone," he said. "We'll rest for a few minutes."

9

As the animals rested they were startled to hear scuffling noises behind them. A group of cats emerged from a pile of cardboard boxes where they had been sleeping. "Keep the noise down!" said one with big, yellow eyes. He looked the Farthing Wood animals up and down. "What do you lot want round 'ere?" he asked.

"We're looking for food," said Fox.

"That's right," Toad added. "Isn't there a big place around here where they throws out food in big metal bin things? A super something or other, they calls it."

"That'll be the supermarket," said the cat. He looked at the other cats and winked slyly, though the Farthing Wood animals did not see him. His yellow eyes narrowed. "We'll show these country animals where us city cats find food, won't we, boys?"

"Sure," said another cat, staring so hard at one of the Voles that he scurried out of sight behind Badger. "Come with us."

The animals followed the cats through a maze of alleyways until they came to a big open space behind a huge building. "The food's round that corner, in big bins," said one cat.

Badger whispered to Fox. "I don't like this. I don't trust these cats."

"Neither do I," said Fox. "But what can we do? We must get some food." He turned to the small animals. "Wait here in the shadows. We'll bring some food back for you."

Badger, Fox, Vixen and Weasel went to the waste bins and found as much food as they could carry. "Quick as you can!" said Badger. "I don't trust those cats."

Badger was right not to trust the cats. When the Farthing Wood animals went back round the corner into the yard they found the Shrews, Voles, Fieldmice and Rabbits huddled in a corner, shivering with fright. Surrounding them on all sides, claws shining, eyes glinting, ready to pounce, were the city cats.

The bigger animals dropped the food they were carrying and rushed to help their friends. Badger cuffed the yellow-eyed cat with one strong paw

and the cat ran off, crying in pain. Fox and Vixen snapped and snarled at the rest, biting at their heels as the cats fled in a screeching huddle. Weasel chased the last one out of the yard, biting off the fur at the tip of its tail.

Badger checked that none of the small animals had been harmed. The food was forgotten. "Come on," he said. Just then a huge container truck rumbled into the supermarket yard and the animals had to scurry away to avoid being hit. "Let's get out of here," Badger said.

Fox led the animals back towards the hill outside the town. They were very frightened and rushed along as quickly as they could, looking this way and that. Traffic roared by, street lights gave them few dark corners to hide in,

and angry-sounding dogs barked loudly. Danger seemed to be everywhere.

Soon the houses were further apart, and there were more trees and green spaces. They were nearly out of the city.

Outside a hotel Toad suddenly stopped. He had just seen something he remembered. "Wait, Fox," he said. "I think we're going to eat after all. Them bins over there, there'll be food in them or my name's not Toad. The humans put leftover food in them and big lorry things come and take it away."

Fox looked at the sky. It was turning pale pink behind the hill. Soon dawn would break and bring new dangers with it. They had to get back to the countryside soon. "Are you sure?" he asked Toad.

Toad nodded his head. "Come on." He led the animals to a line of

dustbins. Badger knocked the lid off one and Weasel jumped inside. He threw out vegetables and bread. Fox knocked another lid off and lifted out some meat bones. There was plenty of food for all the animals and they nibbled and gnawed hungrily.

Just as they had finished eating they heard a rumbling, roaring sound and a huge bin lorry rumbled into the hotel grounds. The animals hurried away and hid in the bushes until it had gone.

They were back in the countryside as dawn broke over the hill. Fox and

Badger led the animals to a safe place in a small clump of trees where they could rest for the day until night fall.

"I'm glad to be out of that city place," said Weasel.

"Me, too, matey," said Toad, rubbing his big round tummy. "But at least we're full now."

Badger nodded. "Yes, but I hope we never have to go to the city again. Like I said before, it's no place for wild animals like us. We need to find a safe place to live, and that place is White Deer Park."

All about Squirrels

Grey Squirrels belong to the animal family called rodents. They are like rats and mice in body shape, but have long, bushy tails. They measure about 50cm nose to tip of tail. They have black, bead-like eyes that stick out of their heads so they can see all around.

Like all rodents, squirrels have very long, sharp front teeth for nibbling and gnawing berries, fruits and tree bark. They like eating nuts, and can open hard shells with their teeth, which grow all the time, but are kept to the right size by all the gnawing they do.

Squirrels live in woodland areas and are very acrobatic animals, leaping from tree to tree. Their tails help them to balance and their sharp claws cling on to rough tree bark. On the ground they can run quite fast.

Squirrels rest and sleep in ball-shaped nests called dreys, built at the top of tall trees using twigs, leaves and straw. They spend much of the winter in their warm drey, but come out to find food on warmer winter days. They bury nuts when they are plentiful in autumn and use these stores in the winter when food is not easy to find, digging up the nuts to eat.

Acorns are the grey squirrel's favourite food and they sometimes use a tree stump as a 'table'. If you have ever seen empty acorn 'cups' on a trunk, they are probably the remains of a squirrel's meal. They also eat insects and some birds' eggs.

Masks to Make

Make some easy Farthing Wood animal masks.

To make a Fox mask you will need:

a piece of card about 60cm x 30cm
felt-tip pens, coloured pencils or crayons
a paper clip and scissors

1 Draw the outline shape shown here on your card. Make it big enough to fit over your face.

2 The thin side pieces should be about 4cm wide.

3 Cut out the mask shape carefully.

4 Get a grown-up to help you try on the mask and mark where the eye holes should go. Ask him or her to cut out the eye holes for you. Try the mask on. Do the eye holes need to be a bit bigger? Do this now.

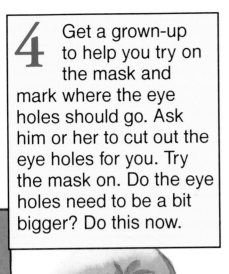

5 Decorate the mask. Use crayons, coloured pencils or felt-tip pens to colour the mask like the one shown here. Use oranges, browns and blacks for Fox's markings. Don't forget the whiskers!

6 When the mask is dry, you can wear it. Put the side pieces around your head and keep them in place with a paper clip.

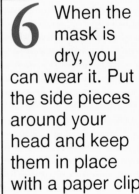

Try making other Farthing Wood animal masks. Copy their markings from pictures in this annual. Those with big ears or eyes work best, like Rabbits, Squirrels, Owl and Toad.

15

1. Spring had arrived. The grass was green, the trees heavy with leaves. Flowers bloomed everywhere and blossom dotted the hedges.

2. The Farthing Wood animals were making good progress on their long journey, now that the nights were warmer and food was easier to find.

3. One day the animals were settling down to rest for the day in a deep, thick hedge when they heard loud whirring, whining noises.

4. They listened in alarm to the ripping, tearing noises. As they listened the noises seemed to come nearer and nearer. What was happening?

5. A thrush hopped into the hedge. She was in a panic. "Can you hear that noise?" she said. "It's the humans. They are cutting down the hedge!"

6. She flapped her wings angrily. "They are cutting down the trees with big chainsaws. Huge digging machines are ripping out all the plants!"

7. "They are just a little way down the lane, and heading this way," said a blue tit. "Let'ssss get out of here, fassst!" hissed Adder.

8. The animals started to move off, but the birds did not move. "We can't go," the thrush explained. "We have all built our nests in the hedge."

9. "Build new ones somewhere else!" said Weasel. "But we have just laid our eggs in the nests," the blue tit said. "We cannot leave them."

10. "Will you help us?" asked the thrush. "We must move the nests to safety." Badger listened as the ripping noises drew closer. "Well?" he asked.

11. Vixen spoke for all the animals. "Of course we'll help," she said. The birds led the animals along the hedge and flew up to their nests in the trees.

12. The squirrels ran up the tree trunks and along the branches. They handed the nests down to the bigger animals as the birds watched anxiously.

13. The bigger animals passed some nests to the smaller animals. The Shrews carried a nest between them. So did the Fieldmice and the Voles.

14. When all the nests were rescued the birds flew off across a ploughed field. They knew a place where their nests would be safe. The animals followed.

15. The birds led the animals to some trees right in the middle of a big field. Soon the nests were safe up in the branches. "Thank you," said the birds.

16. Badger shook his head. "So we are not the only animals whose home has been destroyed by the humans," he said.

All about Shrews

Shrews look like mice, but are even smaller. They measure about 12cm from nose to tail. The one drawn here is actual size, so you can see how tiny that is. They have long, pointed noses or snouts and tiny eyes that look like black beads.

Food is very, very important for shrews. They have to eat their own weight in food EVERY day. Imagine that! They rush around during the night and day, always on the lookout for something to eat. They are insectivores, which means they eat only insects, worms and spiders. They rest for only a few minutes every now and then.

Shrews are active during the day and at night. They are well suited to living in the dark, because though they have very poor eyesight, they have a very good sense of smell and hearing. They find their way around using these senses. Their long, sensitive whiskers help, too, letting them feel their way around in the dark.

and Voles

Voles are covered in silky brown fur. They spend a lot of time grooming their thick fur. They use their long back feet to spread special body oils through it to keep it clean and water repellent. This is important because if a vole's fur became dirty and soggy it would soon die of cold.

The vole is a member of the rodent family of animals. Like all rodents, voles have four very sharp front teeth that are shaped like chisels. They use these to gnaw and nibble at food like stems and leaves, and tree bark in winter. Voles eat insects, too.

Voles live in little burrows lined with grass and moss which they dig in soft ground. Narrow tunnels connect one resting place to another.

Voles are fatter than mice and rats, with a flatter nose and face. They have shorter tails, too. Voles are about 10cm long, with a tail of about 4cm.

Snakes Alive!

"There are lotsss and lotsss of ssnakesss on thissss page. But only two of the sssnakesss are exactly alike. Can you find them?"

The answer is on page 61.

22

It was the middle of a warm summer's night, and stars twinkled and winked in the blue-black sky lit by a yellow moon. Fox, Badger and Toad walked a little way ahead of the rest of the Farthing Wood animals. Toad did not recognize the countryside, and they wanted to make sure that they were going in the right direction that would lead them to White Deer Park.

The ground was high, dry and uneven with very little grass. They had to scramble along from rock to stone, stone to rock.

Toad jumped up on to a tall rock to have a look around. He let out a croak of surprise and beckoned Badger and Fox with his front leg. "'Ere, mateys, come and have a look at this!"

Badger and Fox scrambled up on to the rock where Toad stood. Badger drew in his breath when he saw what Toad was looking at.

Fox blinked quickly and turned to Toad. "What is it?" he asked.

Toad shrugged. "Blessed if I know," he said. "I've never seen the like on it afore now."

What they were looking at was a huge cup shape that looked as if it had been cut out of the hillside. Bare, pale yellow rock was exposed, like a big

bite taken from an apple. The hillside looked as if it had been eaten away by enormous teeth that left no soil, grass or plants behind. The cut-away hillside wasn't dark – it was lit by powerful lamps on top of tall posts that made the dark night brighter than a summer's day. It was noisy, too, with the rumbles, clanks and whines that sounded like some sort of big machine.

The animals looked in wonder as Owl flew up and landed on a tall post a little way in front of them.

DANGER! said a notice nailed to the post. KEEP OUT!

"Do you know what this is, Owl?" asked Fox, waving his paw in the direction of the lights.

Owl knew. She nodded her head. "It's what the humans call a quarry," she said. "They take the stone and rock away in big trucks to build roads and things. That loose stone and rock

down there is probably the stuff they used to fill in the Farthing Wood pond."

The animals were still looking down at the quarry when the smaller animals caught up. They stood staring in wonder. Some cowered back, frightened by the lights and noise.

One of the young Rabbits put his paws over his ears as a loud screech came from the quarry. "Why are they working at night?" he asked. "I thought the humans slept then."

"Some quarries seem to keep working day and night," said Owl. "I think this must be one of them."

"Which way should we go?" asked Weasel.

"I don't think we should go on at all," said Mole. "It's too dangerous. Let's go back the way we came."

"No, we can't," said Fox. "It would take us too long to reach any kind of cover where we can spend the day. We must go on. Look, if we stay on the higher ground we should be able to go around the top edge of the quarry."

Badger nodded his head in

agreement. "Yes, if we can go right round it we'll be able to carry on from the other side. Let's make a start."

Kestrel hovered in the air above them. "I'll fly a little way ahead. That way I can warn you if there is any danger," she said.

"I'll come with you," said Owl.

The animals made their way around the quarry edge. The ground was rough and full of stones and boulders, and the smaller animals found it hard and tiring. The rumbles, booms and screeches of the machines made them all feel nervous, too. They were careful to keep to the shadows.

They were almost to the other side when a loud siren sounded angrily. It sounded just like some sort of large animal in pain. "What'sss that?" hissed Adder nervously.

No one knew. The siren kept sounding. "Come on, let's go on," said Fox.

But as the animals moved off again a huge boom cracked through the night air in the quarry wall below them. It made the animals cower low to the ground. It was followed by another, and another. The rumbling noises that followed seemed to go on for a long time, and huge clouds of pale yellow, choking smoke billowed up around them. Then the ground on the edge of the quarry where they stood seemed to shake and wobble, and the soil beneath their feet slipped away with a loud cracking sound. The men who worked in the quarry had set off explosives

to loosen the rock – but the animals did not know that.

They tried to run away from the edge as it cracked and fell apart, but it was too late. As they scrambled to try to reach firmer ground, the whole side of the quarry slipped away ... and took them with it. They were carried down and down on soft soil and small pieces of stone and rock as if they were on a giant slide.

At last the ground stopped moving and the swirling clouds of dust started to settle. Mole was the first to pick himself up. He couldn't see very well anyway, but he could find things using his nose, and he soon found Badger not far away.

"Are you all right, old friend?" Mole asked.

Badger's fur was not black and white now, but a pale yellow colour. "I think so," he said.

"Good," said Mole. "Let's find the others."

The thick dust at the base of the quarry wall seemed to come to life as the Farthing Wood animals struggled to their feet. They were frightened and a little bit sore, but none of them was injured. The soft dust and stones had given them quite a smooth ride down the steep quarry sides.

Mole and Badger found Fox and

Vixen first, then Weasel, Adder, the Squirrels and the Rabbits. They all helped to dig gently in the dust to free the tiny animals. They choked and coughed, but they were not hurt.

As the animals stood in a frightened, bewildered huddle, Fox counted. Everyone was there.

"What do we do now?" asked Weasel.

"We get out of here, as fast as we can!" said Fox. "We can't climb back up to the top, so we'll just have to take our chance and go across by those buildings."

"But what if the humans see us?" asked Mole.

Fox looked around. All the animals were still covered in pale yellow dust. "They might not see us if we're lucky," he said. "Look, this dust could be a sort of disguise. If we walk against the yellow rock, the humans might not see us."

"Yes, like camouflage," said Owl. "I've only just managed to find you all, and you know how good my eyes are."

So the animals walked around the quarry as quickly as they dared, keeping to the sides of the yard. It was ablaze with lights, but the dust that covered their fur made the animals almost invisible. Hearts beating fast, they hurried and scurried along.

At the big gate Fox held up a paw to stop the others as a huge lorry rumbled past them, making the ground shake. When it had passed the animals slipped outside through the clouds of dust it had made.

Soon the animals were all out in the open countryside again. "What a night!" said Mole, as they stopped to beat the yellow dust from their fur. "The sooner we get to White Deer Park the better!"

"Hear, hear!" said Toad. "Come on!"

The Farthing Wood animals are about to walk through a deep, dark wood. Travel with them by playing this game with a friend.

To the Woods!

Take turns to shake a die, and move along from stone to stone. If you shake a 2, move along 2 stones, and so on.

But remember...
If you land on a **toadstool**, have an extra throw.
If you land on a **flower**, go on 2 spaces.
If you land on a **tree trunk**, miss a turn.
If you land on the **black stone** by the stream, you must shake a 3 before crossing.

The first one to reach the far edge of the wood is the winner.

finish

start

Rescue!

1. One day the animals rested near a big supermarket on the outskirts of a town. "Let's go there tonight," said Mole. "There's food. I can smell it."

2. "I think we should stay away from that place," said Badger. "It's too risky. Remember the trouble we had at that other supermarket with the city cats."

3. Mole could hardly sleep all day. The smells that came from the supermarket waste bins were too much to resist. As darkness fell he slipped away.

4. Later, when the animals were awake and ready for their night's journey, Badger realized that Mole was missing. He had a good idea where he was.

5. "Wait here," Fox and Badger told the others, and they went off to find Mole. They searched near the waste bins, but could find no sign of him.

6. Just then Fox's sharp ears picked up a new sound. A sort of cracking, clanking kind of sound. "Come on," he said. "It's coming from over there."

7. Fox led Badger to three big dome-shaped objects near the car park. The crashing, clanking sounds were coming from the green one.

8. Fox put his paw to his mouth. "Listen," he whispered to Badger. Among the scrambling, clinking noises Badger heard Mole's voice.

9. "Drat and double drat!" said Mole angrily. "There's no food in here, just hundreds of bottles." Mole had fallen into a bottle bank!

10. Badger found a big empty box and climbed up on it. He looked through a hole and saw Mole slithering and sliding around among the bottles.

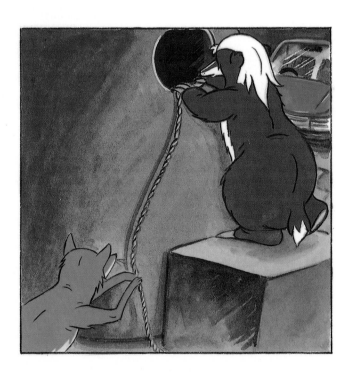

11. Fox handed Badger some string that had been tied around the box. "Hold tight, Mole," said Badger, and he pulled Mole from the bottle bank.

12. "I hope that has taught you a lesson," said Badger. "Yes, now I know where the humans put their bottles of fizzy water! Hic!"

Farthing Wood Facts

How much do you know about the
animals of Farthing Wood?
Answer these questions to find out.
Score one point for each correct answer.

Check your answers on page 61.

1 There are three kinds of Farthing Wood bird.
Owl and Pheasant are two, but what is the third?

2 What is Fox's mate called?

3 What is Mole's favourite kind of food?

4 Which animal likes to tell jokes?

5 Which animal was taken away from
Farthing Wood in a jam jar by humans?

6 What are baby hares called?

7 Near which tree did the animals
meet before they set out on their journey?

8 What is the name of the nature reserve
where the animals hope to make their new home?

9 Which animal is the leader?

10 For one point each, can you fill in
the missing words in the Oath of Mutual Protection
the animals swore before they set off?

"We promise not to - - - - - - - -, bully or - - - each other
on the - - - - journey ahead."

All about Rabbits

Male rabbits are called bucks and females are called does. Their bodies are covered in thick brown-grey fur. They spend a long time cleaning it, using their tongues, teeth and claws to untangle the fur and keep it clean.

Baby rabbits are called kits or kittens. They are born underground. The doe uses soft grass and bits of her own fur to make a cosy nest. There are usually 4 to 8 kits born without fur and with their eyes closed. They are able to look after themselves after about 4 weeks.

Rabbits are always on the lookout for danger. Their big round eyes can see all around, and their long ears can turn this way and that to pick up sounds. They have a good sense of smell, too. The white tip on a rabbit's fluffy tail disappearing down a burrow is a sign to the others that danger is near.

Rabbits spend lots of time underground, in a network of tunnels or burrows called a warren. The round entrances are big enough to let them in and small enough to keep enemies out.

Rabbits eat grass, roots and leaves, nibbling and gnawing with two pairs of long, sharp front teeth. The teeth keep growing, so they gnaw on hard tree bark to keep them the right length.

The Flood

The animals had made good progress, and the sunny summer skies had cheered them on. But now the storm clouds gathered. It had been raining hard for many hours. The animals had travelled through the damp, wet night, and had been forced to take shelter near what was left of an old stone barn that sat on the top of a small hill. It had been abandoned by human beings long ago.

The animals found some old straw inside which was still dry, and were able to make themselves comfortable. They were dry and warm at last.

They were all resting now, apart from Badger and Fox, who stood in the doorway of the barn looking out through the driving rain. "We won't be able to travel on tonight if the rain doesn't stop," said Fox.

"I know," said Badger. "It's too dangerous, especially for the small animals. If their fur gets too wet they'll get very cold. We're safe here for a while. We'll just have to wait for the rain to stop." He pointed to the river that ran through the field just below the hill like a curly snake. "Look at the river. The water is rising all the time."

Fox yawned. "I think we should get some rest now. If the rain stops we'll be able to move on tonight."

Badger agreed, and the two animals settled down with the others to sleep away the day.

35

Badger was woken from his sleep by one of the Rabbits. She was shaking him hard. "Wake up, Badger, please wake up!" she said urgently.

Badger shook his head. "What is it?" he said, instantly alert now.

Rabbit held her paw up. "Listen," she whispered.

Badger listened. He could hear the sound of the rain on what was left of the old slate roof, but there was another sound, too, the sound of water – rushing water, gurgling and swishing.

Badger went to the doorway to investigate. Moonlight glistened on the fields. Some of the grass had disappeared under water. The fields were like one big pond. "I feared this might happen," said Badger. "The river is so swollen with water that it has burst its banks and flooded the fields."

Soon all the animals were wide awake. The small animals clambered up on to window ledges and peered through holes in the stone walls of the barn as moonlight sparkled on what had been grass all around them, and was now water.

Fox and Badger watched from the doorway. "We're stuck here until the water level goes down," said Badger, who had been outside to investigate. "The water is quite deep all around the hill. We'll just have to sit it out."

That night there was a great storm. Loud rumbles of thunder filled the air, and the sky was lit up by zigzag white cracks of lightning. And still the rain fell, pitter pattering on the roof.

The next morning as dawn broke Badger and Fox went outside again. The night before, Badger had pushed a long stick into the ground just below the barn at the water's edge. Now the water came halfway up the stick. "It's much deeper," said Badger. "We're safe for the time being, but what if the water gets even higher?" Fox did not answer...

There was no rest for the animals that day. They were too worried to sleep, and sat, quiet and watchful, as the rain poured down and the water level rose steadily. Things were very serious. They were cut off, surrounded on all sides by the swirling, muddy, thick brown flood water.

As their leader, Fox had a big decision to make. Should they stay,

and hope that the water level would drop eventually, or should they try to escape now? The water was rising by the hour. Some of the animals could swim, but not all of them. The smaller animals would surely drown.

Kestrel and Owl had flown off to find out how bad the flood was. They came back with bad news. Water covered the ground for a long way all around them. Even the animals who could swim would have to swim a long, long way before reaching dry land. Fox sat alone in a corner of the barn and thought hard.

When Badger came back inside from one of his checks on the water level stick he went across to Fox. "Look, I don't know if this will work, but come outside with me, will you?" he asked.

Fox followed Badger to the ruins of an old lean-to shed with a rusty, corrugated iron roof. Badger pointed to two old feeding troughs, and a big water trough. "Do you think we could make them into some sort of boat?" he asked.

Fox turned over one of the troughs. There were small holes in the base. "We might be able to, but we'll have to make them a bit more watertight."

"We could plaster thick mud and grass over the holes, with some of that old plastic sacking inside. What do you think?" asked Badger.

Fox looked up at the rain, which still fell heavily. "I think it's our best chance of getting out of here," he said. "We'll give it a try. Tell the others."

37

Soon the animals had dragged the troughs inside the barn and were busily sealing the holes with grass, thick sticky mud and pieces of old plastic sack.

Badger stood in the doorway to look at the finished boats. "We should leave now," he said.

The larger animals helped the smaller animals to get into the feeding troughs, then they jumped into the big water trough. Fox tried to reassure the tiny animals who sat huddled in fright in the bottom of the troughs. "Don't worry," he said. "I'm going to push you off into the deeper water. There is quite a strong current in the water, so it should keep us all together. We're bound to get to dry ground in the end."

Fox pushed the trough boats into the water, then leapt into the water trough as it bobbed away into the current. The swirling, sloshing water buffeted and tossed the boats around, rocking this way and that, and water sloshed over the side.

The terrible journey seemed to last all night. It was frightening in the darkness of night. But the boats stayed afloat.

The water trough was ahead of the others and Fox had to shout over the noise of the rushing water to make

himself heard. "I think I can see dry land ahead!"

"Well done, shipmates," Toad told the small animals in his trough. "Not long now."

One by one the boats ran up against the dry ground that rose up above the flooded valley. All the animals clambered out, glad to feel solid ground under their paws again. They were wet and frightened – but safe.

"What now?" asked Weasel.

Badger had another idea. "Tip the troughs up to get the water out, and leave them upside down." The animals did as he said, and Badger wedged a stone under one side of each trough. The troughs made good places to shelter them from the rain.

All the animals scrambled under cover. Badger and Mole were last of all. As he got under the trough Mole turned to Badger. "Have you noticed anything?" asked Mole.

Badger shook his head.

Mole held out his paw. "It's stopped raining!" he cried. "Hurrah!"

Badger looked up at the sky. Mole was right. It had stopped raining at last. "We'll rest here until the flood water goes down, then we must carry on to White Deer Park."

Badger and Mole crawled under the trough and, like the other animals, were soon fast asleep.

Paper Plate Puppets

Why not make some Farthing Wood puppets? You could act out one of the stories with your friends.

For each puppet you will need:

2 paper plates   sticky tape
card   felt-tip pens

1 Stick the two plates together with small strips of sticky tape. The base of each plate should be on the **outside**. Leave an opening big enough for your hand to fit inside.

2 Paint or draw an animal face on one of the plates. Keep the opening for your hand at the bottom. Toad and Mole are shown here. Copy their features – eyes, nose and mouth, and colour their fur or skin.

3 Slip your hand inside and make the puppets move!

4 To make puppets of the Farthing Wood animals with pointy ears, cut out two triangles of card for each one. Old cereal boxes are fine. Tape the card ears in place before colouring your puppet. Copy details and marking from the pictures on these or other pages in the annual.

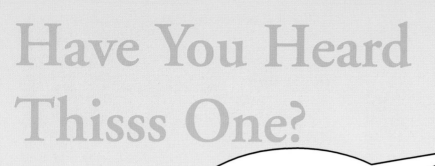

Have You Heard Thisss One?

"My friend Weasssel isssn't the only one who tellsss jokesss! Here are sssome of my favouritesss!"

Why can't you fool a snake?
Because he hasn't got a leg to pull!

What is Toad's favourite flower?
A croakus!

What is green and goes dot dot dot, dash dash dash, dot dot dot?
A Morse Toad.

What do hedgehogs like eating best?
Prickled onions!

What is the difference between Weasel and a stoat?
Weasel is weasily wecognized and a stoat is stoatally different.

I've got a joke, too. Did you hear what happened when Adder caught a cold?
She adder viper nose!

The Bonfire

1. Summer was nearly over and autumn was on its way. The wind was stronger, the nights colder, and the leaves were starting to turn from green to brown.

2. All the animals were tiring of their long, long journey. Every night Fox found it more difficult to encourage them to keep going forward.

3. It was the time of year when many of the smaller animals should have been busily preparing food and shelter for their long winter sleep.

4. Mr and Mrs Hedgehog were tired of walking. All they wanted to do was to curl up into tight balls somewhere warm and cosy and go to sleep.

5. Even the Squirrels, who would not sleep right through the coming winter, wanted to build a nest and collect nuts and acorns to eat later.

6. Vixen tried to encourage Mr and Mrs Hedgehog to go on. "You can't stay here," she said. "It isn't safe. You will probably be dead before spring."

7. The animals walked through the night, and rested beside a clearing for the day. But that night as dusk fell the Hedgehogs refused to go on.

8. "We mussst leave them here then," hissed Adder. "I want to sssleep, too, but it'sss not sssafe here. We mussst go on to White Deer Park."

9. "And we must go on together," said Fox. "All of us. Remember the Oath of Mutual Protection we all swore?" The animals nodded wearily.

10. Mole had an idea. "Why not let the Hedgehogs stay here just for tonight and tomorrow? They might feel able to go on then." Fox agreed to the plan.

11. Mr and Mrs Hedgehog and the small animals crawled under a huge pile of wood in the clearing. Adder curled up in a tin box that sat nearby.

12. The larger animals rested under some bushes. But they did not rest for long. They were woken by loud shrieks, cries and calls. Humans!

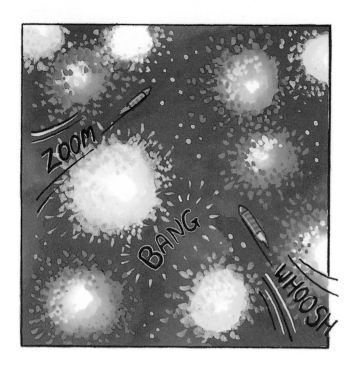

13. Loud zooming, swishing noises were coming from the clearing. Bangs sounded and the sky lit up with tiny coloured explosions of light.

14. The humans were having fun letting off their fireworks for bonfire night. But the animals didn't know that! They were very frightened.

15. Fox poked his snout through the bushes. "The humans are setting the big pile of wood on fire!" he said. "We must get the small animals out!"

16. But how? Toad volunteered to try. He waited until an extra large rocket exploded. As the humans watched it he hopped to the bonfire, unseen.

17. Toad found the small animals shaking with fright as the flames came closer. He waited for another rocket to explode. "Follow me! Now!" he cried.

18. Toad led the animals to the safety of the bushes. "Adder! Come on!" he called as they scurried past the tin. Adder slithered after them.

19. "Are you all right?" Badger asked. "My tail fur is a bit burned," said a Vole. "And my paws feel hot and sore," said a baby Fieldmouse.

20. "We must travel on to White Deer Park right now," said Fox. "There is no time to lose." And this time Mr and Mrs Hedgehog didn't argue with him.

Winter Sleepyheads

Winter is a hard time for lots of animals. They need lots of extra energy to keep warm during the cold, icy weather of the winter months. They get that energy from food. But winter is the time of year when food is very hard to find. The grass does not grow, and roots and shoots are scarce.

Some animals avoid the winter by sleeping right through the cold months. They build a warm, cosy place such as a nest or burrow, curl up and go to sleep. Because sleeping does not use up much energy, they can survive the cold until the warmer weather of spring arrives. This long winter sleep is called hibernation.

Animals that are going to hibernate eat lots of extra food in the autumn so that they grow round and fat. The fat stored in their bodies helps them sleep through the winter without having to eat. The fat is like a food store inside their bodies.

Hedgehogs find a sheltered place at the start of winter and roll themselves up into a tight ball. You should always check a bonfire before it is lit to make sure there are no hedgehogs sleeping there. They live on the fat stored in their bodies. Their 5,000 sharp prickles make sure that no animal enemy disturbs them!

Toads hibernate, too. They sleep in a warm place on land, often under a thick blanket of leaves.

When adders hibernate they often choose a burrow which has been left by another animal to rest in.

Hibernation Crossword

Try this crossword. All the answers are animals that hibernate.
Fit the names of the animals drawn here into the grid.

Here are the words you need:

bat   dormouse
toad   hedgehog
bear   adder   newt

The answer is on page 61.

49

All about Fieldmice

From the tip of his whiskery nose to the end of his long tail a fieldmouse measures about 20cm. His sleek fur is orangey-brown, with a white tummy. Like most members of the mice family, he has big round eyes that look like black buttons. He can see all around him, and can spot danger very quickly. His big ears can pick up the quietest sounds.

Fieldmice are very quick and agile. They are good climbers, leapers and jumpers.

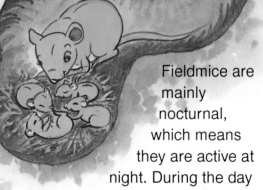

Fieldmice are mainly nocturnal, which means they are active at night. During the day they rest in short undergroud tunnels or under logs. They usually build their nests underground, lining them with torn-up grass and leaves. Fieldmouse babies are born helpless but are able to look after themselves when they are about three weeks old.

Like mice, fieldmice belong to the rodent family of animals. They use their big, sharp front teeth to gnaw foods like nuts and seeds. They like berries, especially hawthorn and blackberry. They sometimes eat small insects, too.

Fieldmice don't just live in fields, but in woods and forests, too. Some people call them Woodmice.

Woodland Word Square

Can you find the names of ten trees and wild flowers in the word square?

They are written up, down, backwards and forwards, and one from corner to corner!

These are the words you need to find:

ACORN ✓ ASH ✓ BEECH ✓
BLACKBERRY ✓ BUTTERCUP ✓
CLOVER ✓ DAISY ✓ ELM ✓
HAWTHORN ✓ OAK ✓

A	R	G	T	F	H	L	N	R	S
B	L	A	C	K	B	E	R	R	Y
Z	E	S	O	N	U	P	O	Q	S
P	Q	E	B	M	T	O	H	E	I
O	A	K	C	E	T	O	T	L	A
Y	D	C	U	H	E	N	W	M	D
B	E	X	G	W	R	I	A	M	L
R	E	V	O	L	C	H	H	S	A
A	C	F	D	V	U	U	I	T	K
A	C	O	R	N	P	J	J	K	L

The solution is on page 61

51

The Lost Sheep

1. The autumn weather was growing colder. The animals were struggling to walk against the biting wind that blew across the wild, open moor.

2. Vixen's keen ears picked up a different sound above that of the wind. She knew what it was. It was the faint bleating cry of a sheep.

3. "But what is a sheep doing up here at this time of year?" asked Fox. "The rest of the flock would have been taken down to the valley days ago."

4. "It must be in trouble," said Badger. "Spread out. We'll soon find it." They did – the sheep had fallen into a deep hole between tussocks of grass.

5. The sides of the hole were so steep and the sheep so heavy that the animals could not get it out. "We can't leave it here," said Badger. "It will die."

6. Dawn was starting to break when Badger heard another sound. "Hear it? A dog, barking. I bet it's the farmer's dog. They'll be searching for the sheep."

7. "Bark, Fox, to attract its attention," said Badger. Fox didn't like farmers, their guns or their dogs but he agreed as long as they could leave right away.

8. Fox barked urgently and the farmer and his dog soon approached through the gloom. The sheep was safe. Badger led the animals off into the cruel wind.

53

40 SUPER PRIZES TO BE WON!

20 winners receive:
a 60-PIECE JIGSAW PUZZLE from Michael Stanfield
20 winners receive:
a 100-PIECE JIGSAW PUZZLE from Michael Stanfield

Michael Stanfield toys and games are available at all major toy shops and superstores.

HOW TO ENTER

It's easy! All you have to do is answer this simple question:

In this book there is a story called *Rescue*!
Who was rescued from the bottle bank in the story?

Write the answer on a postcard or envelope, with your name, age and address.

Send to:
Farthing Wood Competition, Marketing Department, Egmont Publishing, PO Box III, Great Ducie Street, Manchester M60 3BL.

Closing date: Ist February 1996.

The first 40 correct entries selected at random after the closing date will win a prize.

RULES
Employees of World International or their respective agents may not enter this competition.
The Editor's decision is final and no correspondence will be entered into.
A list of winners' names will be available on request and on receipt of a SAE
after I4th February 1996. The Publishers reserve the right to vary the prizes,
subject to availability at the time of judging the competition.

Safe at Last

It was a miserable time for the Farthing Wood
animals. The weather was growing colder, the
nights were growing longer and the days shorter.
The skies were grey and the trees were almost
bare of leaves. Finding enough food every day was
becoming a problem.

Toad, Adder and Mr and Mrs Hedgehog knew
that soon they must hibernate, take their
long winter sleep. But they also knew
that it was not safe to go to sleep just
anywhere – they had to find a safe,
secure place. And Toad more than the
others knew where that place was –
White Deer Park.

The animals settled down in a deep,
dark forest plantation of fir trees to rest
for the day after a long, cold night's walk. It was
cold, quiet, dark and gloomy, but it felt quite safe.

Mrs Hedgehog threw herself down on the carpet of fallen fir
tree needles that covered the floor of the forest. She sighed a
deep sigh. She looked as if she might cry. "I just don't know
how much longer I can go on," she said. "You may have to leave
me here, and go on without me."

"I know jusssst how you feel," said Adder, curling up in a knot of tree roots. "I am exhaussssted."

Toad was also feeling very tired and weary, but he tried to cheer up the others. "I knows it's a long, 'ard journey I've brought you on, but I knows it'll be worth it. Remember, I've seen White Deer Park." He sniffed the chilly air. "And somehow I think we're quite close. I sorta feels it in me bones."

Fox overheard his words. He looked from one animal to another. They lay sprawled where they had stopped, lying on the pine needles that covered the earth, too tired to find more secluded resting places. "I hope you're right, Toad," he said sadly. "I really do."

The animals were not allowed to rest for very long. Weasel's keen ears were the first to pick up the harsh, grating, whirring and ripping sounds that soon woke all the animals. They looked this way and that, in a panic. The noises seemed to be coming towards them from every direction.

There was a loud crashing, swishing sound from overhead, and the tip of a tall fir tree crashed down into the clearing, narrowly missing the

Fieldmice, who had to scurry away quickly.

Toad knew what was happening. "It's them there humans again," he said.

Adder hissed angrily. "Isssn't it alwaysss?" she said.

Toad explained. "The humans plant these trees. They let them grow, then they comes and cuts them down. I've seen them doing it. They use mean, nasty machines with sharp knife things on the front. They can cut through a tree trunk faster than Mole can chew through a root. Honest."

Badger nodded. "Yes, remember when they cut down the hedge with their nasty machines?"

The animals looked at one another. Yes, they remembered having to rescue the birds' nests as their hedge was ripped up.

"This is no place for us," said Badger. As he spoke the tip of another fir tree whooshed past his ear and landed with a thud on the ground. The small animals scurried this way and that, not knowing where to run to find safety.

Fox, Vixen and Badger shepherded the animals together to one side of the clearing. Fox turned to Toad, who was their guide. "Which way?" he asked urgently.

Toad was thinking hard. He had been in a forest like this one before, and he was beginning to think that this was the very same forest. The forest he remembered was very close to White Deer Park. He hardly dared hope, but perhaps, just perhaps...

Toad pointed his foot bravely in front of him. "This way," he said. "Be brave, me hearties. Follow me."

Toad led the animals through the tightly packed tree trunks. The noises of the cutting machines still seemed to be all around them. "Hurry," said Fox, who walked at the back, making sure

that no one was left behind. Badger carried Mole on his back, and the smaller animals scurried along as fast as they could.

They ran and slithered, scurried and hopped, until at last the noises were not so loud. The trees thinned and the animals saw the bright autumn sun again. Soon they had left the last of the trees behind and were in an area of rough gorse bushes.

Fox ran to the front of the group and held up his paw. "We can rest now," he told Toad, who was panting hard. "We're out of the forest now. We seem to have left the humans behind. Well done, Toad, old friend."

The animals threw themselves down on the ground. When Fox had got his breath back he went off to have a look around, for he had seen a fence up ahead, a wire fence, and a very high one. He looked this way and that way. The fence stretched as far as the eye could see.

Owl and Kestrel hovered overhead. They realized what the problem was at once. "I'll fly this way," said Owl. "You go that way, Kestrel. We'll find out how far the fence goes, Fox."

They soon flew back. "It stretches a long way this way," said Owl.

"And the other," said Kestrel.

Badger, Toad and some of the other animals came to find out what was going on. Dusk had fallen now, and a sparkling of frost had appeared on the fence, the grass and the gorse bushes. Fox told them about the fence.

As the animals looked this way and

that, Toad looked thoughtful. There was something very familiar about this place. He looked to one side. There was a piece of wood high up on the fence. It looked like a sign of some sort, but Toad could not see it clearly as it was covered in spangles of white frost that started to twinkle and shine now as night fell. "Squirrel, run up the fence, will you, and wipe that frost off?" he asked.

Squirrel did as Toad asked. As he wiped away the cold, hard frost, the animals saw more of the sign. It was dark green, and on it was a white shape. As Squirrel rubbed away the frost Toad held his breath. When Squirrel wiped away the last of the frost Toad leapt into the air. "Look!" he cried. "Look! It's a sort of picture. A picture of a deer. A WHITE deer!" He turned to the others. "We're here. This is White Deer Park!" The others could hardly believe it, but they looked at the sign. Yes, the picture was clear now. A white deer. They looked at each other happily. They had reached their new home. They were safe at last.

But Badger didn't look very happy. There was still the problem of the fence. The smaller animals could easily squeeze through the gaps in the fence, but what about the bigger ones? How would they get through?

It was very dark now, and the night looked like being a cold one. "Look, whoever can squeeze through, get

through now," Badger told the smaller animals.

The Shrews, Voles, and Fieldmice wriggled through easily. Mole, Adder, Toad and Weasel just about managed to push themselves through too, though it was a tight squeeze for Toad and Weasel. That left Badger, Fox, Vixen and the Rabbits outside White Deer Park. They couldn't climb the fence, because it was far too steep and high. Then Badger had one of his good ideas. He whispered to Toad through the fence, and Toad nodded his head excitedly. "Yes, yes, why didn't I think of that?" said Toad. He pointed to his right. "Yes, Badger, it's along that way."

"Won't be a minute, Fox," said Badger, and he beckoned the Rabbits to follow him.

Fox and Vixen watched them scurrying off, and wondered what was going on.

Badger and the Rabbits were soon back, and they were carrying a long plank of wood between them, the

58

Rabbits at the front and Badger at the back. "I realized if the humans were cutting down the trees, they must store the wood nearby," he explained. "Toad told me where the wood yard is. That's where we found this."

Fox still didn't understand until Badger got the others to help him lift the plank of wood up into the air. It wobbled this way and that, but finally they managed to rest one end of the plank on the very top of the wire fence. It made a sort of platform leading up from the ground.

Inside White Deer Park, Weasel suddenly realized what Badger was going to do, and organized the small animals. He sent them off in all directions and they came back with armfuls of fallen leaves and pine needles. Soon they had built a huge pile of leaves up against the fence. "Well done, Weasel!" said Badger.

Now Fox realized what was going on, too. "I suppose you expect us to climb that piece of wood to the top of the fence and jump off at the end?" he asked.

Badger nodded. "Yes. That's it. Now, who's going to be first?"

A Rabbit stepped forward. He moved carefully along the plank in little hops, higher and higher. The wood was a little slippery with frost, but at last he was at the top. The pile of leaves looked a long, long way down. "Go on!" said Badger, and Rabbit jumped. He disappeared for a few seconds. Then his head appeared and he smiled. He had had a very soft landing.

The rest of the Rabbits were soon safe inside White Deer Park. Fox and Vixen were next. They had to grip hard to stop themselves from sliding back down the plank, but at last they were safely over. Last of all came Badger, who made his way slowly but steadily to the top. He launched himself off and landed with a soft thud in the pile of leaves.

The animals stood looking around. They could hardly believe that they had reached their new home. "Well done, Fox, our leader, and Toad, our guide," said Badger. "Well done, everyone."

But there was no time for celebration. The first frost meant that winter was on its way, and the animals had to make preparations. Toad, the Hedgehogs and Adder said goodbye until spring and went off to find warm places where they could sleep through the cold winter months.

The Squirrels set about collecting twigs and sticks to make a nest in the trees, and acorns for their food store.

Fox, Vixen, Badger, Mole and the Rabbits had to dig burrows and tunnels under the ground so that they would have warm homes for the winter. All the animals had work to do, and knew that time was short.

Their long journey had a been a hard and sometimes dangerous one, but they had found safety in White Deer Park. One by one, as frost spangled the bare trees and the red sun of dawn broke over a hill, they scurried and hurried off to their new homes.

Answers

page 22 Snakes Alive!
Snakes **b** and **h** are the same.

page 33 Farthing Wood Facts
1. Kestrel
2. Vixen
3. Earthworms
4. Weasel
5. Toad
6. Leverets
7. The Great Beech
8. White Deer Park
9. Fox
10. Frighten, eat, long

How did you score?

9-12 points	You are a true Farthing Wood friend!
5-8 points	Well done, you know a lot about the animals!
less than 5 points	Why not read the annual again and see if you can improve your score?

page 49 Hibernation Crossword
1 down: newt
2 across: adder
3 down: dormouse
4 down: hedgehog
5 down: bat
6 across: bear
7 across: toad

page 51 Woodland Word Square

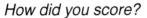

A	R	G	T	F	H	L	N	R	S
B	L	A	C	K	B	E	R	R	Y
Z	E	S	O	N	U	P	O	Q	S
P	Q	E	B	M	T	O	H	E	I
O	A	K	C	E	T	O	T	L	A
Y	D	C	U	H	E	N	W	M	D
B	E	X	G	W	R	I	A	M	L
R	E	V	O	L	C	H	H	S	A
A	C	F	D	V	U	U	I	T	K
A	C	O	R	N	P	J	J	K	L